WARM-UP EXERCISES

Calisthenics for the Brain
Book I

by

Rita Kisner

and

Brooke Knowles

Thinking Publications
Eau Claire, WI

Printed in the United States of America

02   01   12   11   10   9   8

ISBN 0-9610370-8-3

**THINKING
PUBLICATIONS**
A Division of McKinley Companies, Inc.

424 Galloway Street
Eau Claire, WI 54702-0163
(715) 832-2488
FAX (715) 832-9082

About the Authors

Rita Kisner received both her B.A. and M.A. in communication disorders from California State University, Fullerton. She has worked as a speech-language pathologist in the schools and as a special day classroom teacher for students with language disorders. Ms. Kisner was involved with the Communicatively Handicapped Adolescent Program, CHAP, a pilot program in the Fullerton Union High School District, for two years before joining the Huntington Beach Union High School District in 1978. Although Ms. Kisner has worked with all age groups, her primary area of interest remains with the adolescent population.

Brooke Knowles received her B.A. in speech communication from the University of Southern California and her M.A. in communicative disorders from California State University, Long Beach. She has worked as a speech-language pathologist on the adolescent unit of a private psychiatric hospital, consultant to physical therapists in child stimulation, consultant on effective communication to employees of a major corporation, and teacher-trainer in "Effective Classrooms." She is presently employed by the Huntington Beach Union High School District as a speech-language pathologist.

Acknowledgments

We would like to thank Don Gates, a former student, who helped set up and copy our original book, and Dick and Jerry of Rudi's Repros for patiently running double-sided copies of the various rewrites over the last five years.

Our thanks also to Marie Otto, Acting Superintendent of Huntington Beach Union High School District, for creating a climate which is supportive of our profession.

A very special thanks to my own adolescent, my son, Mark Kisner. He has been the joy of my life, my personal "control group," my critic, and my moral support; and thanks to my family and very special friends for truly believing that I can do anything.

Thank you, Jim Knowles, for honoring our commitment to not hinder one another, but to "bring out the best in me and in you, too." I deeply appreciate your unfailing support, admiration, and joy in being the other side of my "win."

Most of all, we are indebted to our high school students, past, present, and future, for making it all worthwhile. Thank you.

Introduction

Warm-Up Exercises Book I was designed for adolescents and young adults. This is not a cookbook approach to language remediation and is not intended to replace or change the objectives for an individual class or student. These exercises are intended to function as warm-ups, calisthenics for the brain.

We have found them to be an effective way to set the tone at the beginning of a class or session and to make the remainder of the intervention session or class more productive. Our students enjoy the predictability of these exercises. Instead of asking, "What are we going to do today?" our students are busy preparing themselves for the first activity.

Current research and our experience have shown that adolescents with learning and language disabilities have language deficiencies that are combined and interwoven rather than isolated. Although goals are written for specific areas of need, there is rarely sufficient time to remediate all the areas of language that are deficient. These warm-up exercises briefly cover many areas of need not specifically addressed in language objectives.

We recognize that all areas of language are closely related and that a deficit in one area may subtly affect all other areas. For the purpose of these exercises, however, it was necessary for us to delineate the major components that are thought to make up language. The areas of auditory perception, classification, semantics, and syntax/morphology were chosen based on the conceptual framework of language discussed by Wiig and Semel (1976).

1

Although the validity of the remaining two areas, auditory memory and general questions, may be questioned, we feel their inclusion is justified. While there is little evidence in the literature to support that auditory memory remediation improves language functioning, we have included it and placed it first for a number of reasons. The students are familiar with these types of exercises because memory tasks are still included on many standardized tests of language and cognitive ability. Since this is a rote activity, the exercises require little more than a simple automatic response and function to gain the students' attention in an enjoyable and nonthreatening way.

The category of General Questions was chosen as a partial answer to increasing our students' funds of knowledge. Many of the questions are based upon junior and senior high school course work (e.g., geography, history, math, and physical education). Others are based upon spatial, temporal, or familial relationships. Some questions involve divergent thinking processes, others convergent thinking processes. And we must admit, some were included just for fun!

As you become familiar with the exercises, you will find they provide an excellent means for:

1. reviewing and reinforcing previously learned language skills;

2. supplementing an ongoing intervention program; and

3. identifying subtle language difficulties through informal observation.

Introduction

Although *Warm-Up Exercises* were not designed to take the place of a comprehensive language program, an Item Analysis is included which provides quick access to all exercises in a specific area.

We have provided answers to most of the exercise questions. In many instances, there is only one possible answer (e.g., the Eiffel Tower can only be found in France). For a number of the exercises, we have marked the most common response, but not necessarily the only correct one. The Classification section of Warm-Up #15 is an example. *Broom* and *mop* are marked as the correct response, however, *tea* and *water* would also be acceptable. Any answer that the student can justify and explain should be accepted as correct since the purpose of these exercises is to provide calisthenics for the brain.

While we developed these exercises primarily for use with adolescents who have language disorders, other professionals have also found them to be beneficial. For example, classroom teachers have used these by designating one student to present the exercise to the class thereby freeing the teacher for such mundane but necessary chores as taking roll, marking tardies, and handing back homework. Classroom teachers have also found *Warm-Up Excercises* to be valuable during the final minutes of class while the students (and the teacher!) are waiting for the bell to ring.

Teachers in special education and remedial classes use these exercises in much the same way. They have also used them as an independent small group activity.

Warm-Up Exercises Book I

We have used these *Warm-Up Exercises* for years because they work! We hope they will become an integral part of your classes and remediation sessions, too.

References

Wiig, E., and Semel, E. (1976). *Language disabilities in children and adolescents*. Columbus, Ohio: Charles E. Merrill.

Item Analysis

AUDITORY MEMORY Excercise No.

Repeat numbers forward 1, 2, 3, 4, 5

Repeat numbers backwards 6, 7, 8, 9

Unrelated words.....................................10, 11, 12, 13, 14, 15

Repeat sentences...16, 17, 18, 19, 20, 21, 22, 23, 24, 25, 26, 27, 28

Scrambled sentences...29, 30, 31, 32, 33, 34, 35, 36, 37, 38, 39

Nonsense sentences 40, 41, 42, 43, 44, 45, 46, 47, 48, 49, 50

AUDITORY PERCEPTION

Auditory closure....................6, 9, 11, 14, 24, 28, 36, 42, 45, 48

Sound blending 2, 4, 22, 25, 30, 31, 32, 34, 38, 40

Syllable count 1, 8, 13, 17, 26, 39, 44, 49

Rhyming words.......3, 10, 15, 18, 20, 21, 27, 29, 35, 37, 47, 50

Words beginning with a sound 5, 7, 12, 16, 19

Words ending with a sound 23, 33, 41, 43, 46

CLASSIFICATION

Add a word to a category 6, 10, 22, 25, 33, 34, 41, 49

Analogy 13, 19, 20, 23, 30, 32, 46, 50

Likeness/Difference 7, 8, 12, 24, 31, 38, 48

Two characteristics...2, 5, 14, 16

What category..11, 26, 36, 44

Which one doesn't belong 1, 3, 9, 18, 21, 28, 35, 47

Which two go together ...4, 15, 17, 27, 29, 37, 39, 40, 42, 43, 45

Warm-Up Exercises Book I

AUDITORY MEMORY

Repeat these numbers.

7-4-2-3	5-3-6-7-1
1-0-6-5	3-3-5-7-1-4
2-5-7-3-5	4-1-7-2-6-9

AUDITORY PERCEPTION

How many syllables are in the word?

afternoon (3)

basketball (3)

conditioner (4)

Colorado (4)

transportation (4)

experiment (4)

CLASSIFICATION

Which one doesn't belong?

apple - carrot - broccoli - cabbage

dog - cat - *shark* - whale

chair - sofa - *glass* - table

dish - fork - cup - *placemat*

hammer - *nails* - screwdriver - axe

house - *car* - tent - trailer

SEMANTICS

Give a word that means the same as:

adult

difficult

wonderful

courteous

cautious

genuine

SYNTAX/MORPHOLOGY

Is this sentence correct?

The fireworks are the most noisiest of all.

The temperature was the coldest I've felt.

This horse is the best one of the bunch.

This freeway is more wider than that one.

She is the saddest girl in town.

Is 10 morer than 9?

GENERAL QUESTIONS

What direction would you have to travel to reach:

the equator

the North Pole

the South Pole

the Atlantic Ocean

Alaska

Japan

Warm-Up #2

AUDITORY MEMORY
Repeat these numbers.

7-3-6-4	6-1-7-5-8
2-9-5-8	9-2-6-5-1-4
3-7-5-2-9	5-5-6-8-7-7

AUDITORY PERCEPTION
What is this word?

a-n-t

b-a-b-y

v-i-n-e-g-ar

pr-o-gr-a-m

r-e-s-p-o-n-s-i-ble

s-u-g-ar

CLASSIFICATION
Name something that is:

small and round

large and lightweight

sweet and red

flat and breakable

long and sharp

cold and white

SEMANTICS
Give two meanings for these words.

      heard, herd

      fire

      wait, weight

      left

      Mary, merry, marry

      where, wear

SYNTAX/MORPHOLOGY
Change these words to mean more than one.

      person

      wolf

      scissors

      brother-in-law

      piece of paper

      fly

GENERAL QUESTIONS
Answer these questions.

      What are the names of two colleges or universities?

      What are two liquids that you put in a car?

      What do we call water in its solid form?

      Who is a famous painter?

      What shape do you associate with the pyramids?

      What are three religions?

AUDITORY MEMORY

Repeat these numbers.

8-1-8-6	3-4-0-1-3
4-0-1-6	1-1-3-5-9-2
5-3-3-9-2	9-4-0-7-4-5

AUDITORY PERCEPTION

Give two words that rhyme with:

hop

from

fly

said

ace

sent

CLASSIFICATION

Which one doesn't belong?

quarter - dime - *dollar bill* - penny - nickel

house - apartment - condominium - trailer - *office*

pencil - *paper* - pen - typewriter - crayon

poodle - *Siamese* - collie - spaniel - German shepherd

slippers - socks - shoes - boots - *slacks*

circle - square - rectangle - triangle - hexagon

SEMANTICS

Give a word that means the opposite.

dark

hungry

birth

nervous

poor

answer

SYNTAX/MORPHOLOGY

Is this a complete sentence?

Yesterday at the store.

I went alone.

Running quickly.

How much is it?

The yellow chair by the table.

The picture by the window.

GENERAL QUESTIONS

Answer these questions.

What are two animals with stripes?

What is the name of one of the Great Lakes?

If you drove 30 mph, how far could you go in 10 minutes?

What is the name of a volcano?

Who was Leonardo da Vinci?

What are the names of three birds?

AUDITORY MEMORY

Repeat these numbers.

7-0-1-6-9   1-3-7-6-4-6

9-3-6-8-6   3-6-4-9-2-3-1

2-2-2-4-9-2   9-7-3-9-6-1-7

AUDITORY PERCEPTION

What is this word?

m-e

c-oa-t

w-i-sh

c-a-m-p

n-a-me

p-i-ll-ow

CLASSIFICATION

Which two go together?

chalk - bandage - *board* - finger - tree

hanger - leaves - bread - war - *coat*

canoe - *saddle* - *horse* - music - eraser

razor - film - lipstick - *whiskers* - milk

sneeze - stomach - *purse* - rain - *money*

balloon - *stars* - lake - *telescope* - pepper

SEMANTICS

Quickly name something real or imaginary that would make you feel:

lonely	serious
pleased	annoyed
shocked	sleepy

SYNTAX/MORPHOLOGY

What is the contraction for:

should not

he will

is not

they are

did not

I am

GENERAL QUESTIONS

In what country would I find:

the Eiffel Tower (France)

the Great Pyramids (Egypt)

the Empire State Building (United States)

Big Ben (England)

the Leaning Tower of Pisa (Italy)

the Taj Mahal (India)

Warm-Up #5

AUDITORY MEMORY
Repeat these numbers.

8-3-9-2-1   2-2-5-7-8-3

3-7-2-9-4   3-2-4-7-9-3-6

3-9-2-6-7-4   7-5-9-2-4-1-1

AUDITORY PERCEPTION
Give me a word beginning with this sound.

/b/

/f/

/s/

/k/

/m/

/ʃ/

CLASSIFICATION
Name something that is:

small and electrical

black and hot

small and heavy

cold and liquid

brown and alive

portable and has wheels

SEMANTICS

Give a word that means the same as:

frightened	obese
immense	ancient
filthy	cash

SYNTAX/MORPHOLOGY

Correct these sentences.

The little girl hurt himself.

We will go to the game yesterday.

The dogs chases each other.

Mother fixed me two egg for breakfast.

Bob runned the 400 meter in track.

Him forgot to finish his homework.

GENERAL QUESTIONS

What country would you be visiting if you paid for your lunch with:

pesos (Mexico)

pounds (England)

liras (Italy)

dollars (U.S., Canada)

francs (France, Switzerland)

yen (Japan)

Warm-Up #6

AUDITORY MEMORY
Repeat these numbers backwards.

4-9	8-9-0
6-4	5-3-2-8
3-4-2	8-9-4-3

AUDITORY PERCEPTION
What is this word?

to / orrow (tomorrow)

/ an / e / oupe (cantaloupe, antelope)

/ ultipli / ation (multiplication)

/ en / illion (ten million)

nine / y per / ent (ninety percent)

/ antas / ic (fantastic)

CLASSIFICATION
Add an appropriate word.

bee - beetle - grasshopper (insect)

branch - twig - leaf (part of a tree)

catcher - outfielder - pitcher (baseball team)

spring - fall - summer (season)

pond - ocean - river (body of water)

poodle - golden retriever - German shepherd (dog)

SEMANTICS

Why don't these sentences make sense?

> I was speeding along the freeway at fifteen miles an hour,
> when suddenly I had to stop.
>
> This summer I plan to walk to Hawaii.
>
> My birthday is February 30th.
>
> My father told me to pick up the telephone and listen into
> the receiver.
>
> When I turn eight, I plan to apply for my driver's license.
>
> After school is over, I go home and eat a big breakfast.

SYNTAX/MORPHOLOGY

Change these words to mean more than one.

sand	child
foot	asparagus
buffalo	head of cabbage

GENERAL QUESTIONS

Answer these questions.

> What is the name of a continent?
>
> What is the name of a small animal that does not have fur?
>
> Which state begins with the letter "M"?
>
> What month comes before September?
>
> What kind of store would you go to, to buy Band-Aids?
>
> Which is longer, a meter or a yard?

AUDITORY MEMORY
Repeat these numbers backwards.

5-8-9	8-4-3-1
9-3-8	6-9-3-8-4
8-7-9-2	8-5-3-8-7

AUDITORY PERCEPTION
Give me a word beginning with this sound.

/l/

/p/

/b/

/t/

/w/

/z/

CLASSIFICATION
How are these two alike?

match - flashlight

horse - bicycle

rake - shovel

sock - box

suitcase - purse

sneeze - cough

SEMANTICS

Which is more?

> scared - frightened
>
> hideous - ugly
>
> definite - probable
>
> famished - hungry
>
> mad - irate
>
> depressed - unhappy

SYNTAX/MORPHOLOGY

Is this sentence correct?

> My hands are dirtier than yours.
>
> I have a short rope than you.
>
> It is more better today than yesterday.
>
> His glass is fuller than mine.
>
> This pencil is the sharper of all the pencils.
>
> The teacher is more angrier than I am.

GENERAL QUESTIONS

What occupation do you associate with:

> Frank Lloyd Wright (architect)
>
> Thomas Edison (inventor)
>
> Pablo Picasso (artist)
>
> Ludwig von Beethoven (composer)
>
> William Shakespeare (author)
>
> Florence Nightingale (nursing)

Warm-Up #8

AUDITORY MEMORY

Repeat these numbers backwards.

8-3-9	5-5-4-1
1-7-5	2-4-0-5-3
7-9-8-6	4-3-6-8-9

AUDITORY PERCEPTION

How many syllables are in the word?

photograph (3)

dime (1)

individual (5)

test (1)

arithmetic (4)

helicopter (4)

CLASSIFICATION

How are these two alike?

photograph - painting

bread - cake

seed - bulb

turtle - seashell

sailboat - hang glider

brick - cement

SEMANTICS

Give a word that means the same as:

search

beautiful

glad

complete

difficult

vanish

SYNTAX/MORPHOLOGY

Is this sentence correct?

I go there oftener than he does.

Our team is much more better this year.

Whose hair is longer, Kayla's or Stephanie's?

The fastest runner received the blue ribbon.

I couldn't get much sicker!

More and more faster he ran.

GENERAL QUESTIONS

What kind of tool would you use to:

open a bottle

chop down a tree

clean a floor

attach two pieces of paper

change a tire

remove a screw

AUDITORY MEMORY

Repeat these numbers backwards.

9-7-8   8-3-9-6

3-4-6   3-5-4-2-0

7-8-3-5   3-8-6-2-1

AUDITORY PERCEPTION

What is this word?

/ umpkin (pumpkin)

/ andruff (dandruff)

um / ella (umbrella)

milk / ake (milkshake)

/ as / egas (Las Vegas)

lo / o / otive (locomotive)

CLASSIFICATION

Which one doesn't belong?

volleyball - soccer - baseball - *helmet*

president - king - queen - duke

Kennedy - Carter - *Harper* - Ford

sick - flu - measles - cold

New York - Illinois - Hawaii - *Canada*

oak - sycamore - *basket* - pine

SEMANTICS

Quickly name something real or imaginary that would make you feel:

dejected   attractive

alarmed   deserted

giddy   brilliant

SYNTAX/MORPHOLOGY

Is this a complete sentence?

Fell to the ground.

Makes fine bookmarks.

When are you going?

Come here.

Tall, lovely flowers.

Leave now.

GENERAL QUESTIONS

Answer the following questions.

What could you do with a brick besides build with it?

What could you do with a book besides read it?

What could you do with a cup besides drink from it?

What could you do with chewing gum besides chew it?

What could you do with a baseball bat besides hit a ball with it?

What could you do with a pencil besides write with it?

Warm-Up #10

AUDITORY MEMORY
Repeat these words.

chart - cow - net

cup - clock - girl

chair - root - light - shoe

roof - tree - lock - can

day - door - man - post - floor

red - sky - chalk - leaf - watch

AUDITORY PERCEPTION
Give two words that rhyme with:

mall	stamp
tram	slate
stare	dread

CLASSIFICATION
Add an appropriate word.

German - French - English - Japanese (language or
nationality)

toothpick - pencil - table - chair (made of wood)

hamburger - fries - taco - Coke (fast food)

tomato - apple - grapefruit - cranberry (juice)

France - Spain - Sweden - Norway (European country)

ant - flea - grain of sand - speck of dust (small)

SEMANTICS

Quickly name something real or imaginary that would make you feel:

envious	antagonized
thrilled	confused
infatuated	belligerent

SYNTAX/MORPHOLOGY

Change these to the present tense.

He *walked* the dog.

I *went* to school at Central High School.

She *curled* her hair very nicely.

The dog *jumped* over the fence.

He *wrote* his name in the wrong place.

The clock *ticked* silently.

GENERAL QUESTIONS

Answer these questions.

If you had 50¢ and you wanted to buy a ticket to the football game that cost $2, how much would you have to borrow?

What is the equator?

Which state in the U.S. is farthest west?

What is a fruit that doesn't grow on trees?

What is a sport played during the Summer Olympics?

What is the name of a country in South America?

Warm-Up #11

AUDITORY MEMORY
Repeat these words.

note - cord - mouse

hand - bike - nail

couch - wand - school - night

shorts - wall - sign - stone

fish - plane - wave - boat - seat

board - mail - light - ring - lawn

AUDITORY PERCEPTION
What is this word?

a / ar / ent (apartment)   / arking / ot (parking lot)

/ oyota (Toyota)   / ew / ork (New York)

a / ter / oon (afternoon)   har / onica (harmonica)

CLASSIFICATION
In what category do these belong?

diamond - emerald - opal - ruby - amethyst

carnation - daisy - aster - rose - violet

lipstick - powder - rouge - mascara - eye shadow

Vermont - New York - Minnesota - Kansas - Nebraska

evening - noon - morning - night - midnight

week - century - millenium - year - decade

SEMANTICS

Which is more?

> painful - aching - excruciating
>
> violet - purple - lavender
>
> comatose - faint - unconscious
>
> satisfied - content - fulfilled
>
> odor - stench - scent
>
> superior - good - excellent

SYNTAX/MORPHOLOGY

Change these sentences to the future tense.

> She *walks* to the store.
>
> I *go* play tennis.
>
> After I take a shower, I *dry* my hair.
>
> They *are going* on a picnic in the park.
>
> I *meet* you at the beach.
>
> We *have* a test in American history.

GENERAL QUESTIONS

In what country will I find these major cities?

> London
>
> Toronto
>
> Chicago
>
> Beijing
>
> New York
>
> Paris

Warm-Up #12

AUDITORY MEMORY

Repeat these words.

blue - bed - air - friend

airplane - duck - knife - moon

phone - ladder - fruit - ear - city

book - apple - boot - clock - lamp

picture - egg - coat - bottle - arm - pig

mouse - pillow - plant - nail - leaf - cook

AUDITORY PERCEPTION

Give me a word beginning with this sound.

/g/	/ʃ/
/n/	/dʒ/
/θ/	/v/

CLASSIFICATION

How are these two alike?

chair - bench

hairbrush - toothbrush

igloo - condominium

sail - windmill

bandage - gauze

Congress - Parliament

SEMANTICS

Give two meanings for these words.

made, maid

male, mail

meat, meet

won, one

pear, pair, pare

plane, plain

SYNTAX/MORPHOLOGY

Correct these sentences.

All the trucks is 16-wheelers.

Me and Bob are ready to go.

Superman bended the steel rod.

Lee don't speak English.

I don't got no homework tonight.

Tomorrow we finished cleaning the yard.

GENERAL QUESTIONS

What kind of tool would you use to:

peel a potato

hang a picture

dig a garden

sew a button

get rid of a beard

cut wood

AUDITORY MEMORY

Repeat these words.

toast - nail - pickle - ocean

bell - bone - arrow - hill

fiddle - daisy - feather - punch - clock

cake - board - kite - ice - lead

gold - lamb - grass - eel - church - snow

water - music - tail - head - cloud - work

AUDITORY PERCEPTION

How many syllables are in the word?

assignment (3)   versatile (3)

ambulance (3)   education (4)

surprisingly (4)   presbyterian (5)

CLASSIFICATION

Complete these sentences.

Off is to *on* as *after* is to (*before*).

Place is to *where* as *time* is to (*when*).

Happier is to *happiest* as *better* is to (*best*).

Bedroom is to *sleep* as *kitchen* is to (*cook*).

Rose is to *flower* as *oak* is to (*tree*).

Blow is to *bugle* as *beat* is to (*drum*).

SEMANTICS

Give a word that means the opposite.

below

shallow

loose

generous

plain

reward

SYNTAX/MORPHOLOGY

Change these words to mean more than one.

feather

fish

house

witch

goose

man

GENERAL QUESTIONS

Answer these questions.

What is the name of a dramatic play?

Other than an ocean, what is the name of a body of water
that is salty?

What are three things made out of brick?

What are two countries in the Eastern Hemisphere?

What is a liquid that is not drunk out of a glass?

What are three sections of a newspaper?

Warm-Up #14

AUDITORY MEMORY

Repeat these words.

kite - nest - corn - play - man

farm - bug - ball - bus - hour

butter - feet - log - radio - nut - duck

rain - heart - cup - can - bear - match

bed - cat - deer - flower - horse - mile - cake

rock - chair - food - house - milk - paper - cow

AUDITORY PERCEPTION

What is this word?

e / er /ise (exercise)

a / abet (alphabet)

/ edge ha / er (sledge hammer)

groc / y / ore (grocery store)

/ eftovers (leftovers)

hi / o / o / a / us (hippopotamus)

CLASSIFICATION

Name something that is:

liquid and sticky

long and wooden

small and silver

brown and has a shell

large and valuable

important and made of paper

SEMANTICS

Give two meanings for these words.

break, brake	week, weak
passed, past	shone, shown
threw, through	whose, who's

SYNTAX/MORPHOLOGY

Change these statements to questions that can be answered yes or no.

Mary went to school yesterday.

The mouse ran under the sink.

We had a substitute teacher in math.

Josh passed his driver's test.

Leanne will be gone this weekend.

Robin will have enough money to pay for her car insurance.

GENERAL QUESTIONS

Answer these questions.

What are three sections of a library?

What is liquid but cannot be drunk?

What is another way to say hello?

What could you wear on your head besides a hat?

What are three sections of a department store?

What is a vegetable that grows on a vine?

Warm-Up #15

AUDITORY MEMORY

Repeat these words.

> shoe - cliff - moon - mine - store
>
> apple - beach - bank - fire - lot
>
> burn - closet - dark - board - nut - dust
>
> party - church - card - storm - dance - office
>
> tree - shop - circus - edge - doctor - foot - game
>
> room - cave - fish - dump - hay - bed - hole

AUDITORY PERCEPTION

Give two words that rhyme with:

mop	pink
lunch	same
bride	show

CLASSIFICATION

Which two go together?

> *jelly* - hamburger - *jam* - soda pop
>
> *Chad* - Sue - *John* - principal
>
> *cat* - cabbage - *dog* - airplane
>
> short - *helmet* - coffee - *wig*
>
> water - tea - *broom* - *mop*
>
> *jacket* - eye - pencil - *sweater*

SEMANTICS

Give me a word that means the same as:

pretty	frightened
beneath	difficult
yell	error

SYNTAX/MORPHOLOGY

Change these sentences to the future tense.

The sailboat *sank* in the stormy sea.

I *saw* Rachel after class.

They *flew* to Utah to go skiing.

Dad *hid* Jack's birthday present in the closet.

The bell *rang* at the end of the period.

Chris *did* all of his social studies homework.

GENERAL QUESTIONS

Answer these questions.

What is a method of transportation that does not have wheels?

What could you read that isn't a newspaper, magazine, or book?

What is something that gives light and is not electrical?

What is the name of a vegetable that is not green?

What is another name for autumn?

What could you wear on your feet besides shoes?

Warm-Up #16

AUDITORY MEMORY
Repeat these sentences.

After school, I am going to the store to buy some shoes.

My mother said that I have to be home by 8:00.

Next year, when I am a senior, I am going to take drama.

John's favorite hobbies are snow skiing, jogging, and wrestling.

When I get my own car, I am going to visit my friend in Vermont.

Are you going to attend summer school this year at the junior college?

AUDITORY PERCEPTION
Give me a word beginning with this sound.

/s/	/r/
/t/	/m/
/k/	/d/

CLASSIFICATION
Name something that is:

round and flat

large and full of air

long and glass

square and plastic

valuable and not worth money

paper and covered with numbers

SEMANTICS

Give two meanings for these words.

aisle, I'll, isle

poor, pore, pour

ring, wring

there, their, they're

dear, deer

role, roll

SYNTAX/MORPHOLOGY

Combine these sentences into one sentence.

I have history first period. I have English second period.

I was late for class. I received a tardy notice.

Would you like to watch television? Would you like to play a game?

I like to swim. I don't like to swim when the water is cold.

Go to the store. Buy some milk.

I like chocolate. I don't like ice cream.

GENERAL QUESTIONS

What do we call the natives of each of these countries?

France	Russia
Italy	Thailand
Canada	U.S.A.

Warm-Up #17

AUDITORY MEMORY
Repeat these sentences.

> I wish I didn't have to share a room with my brother.
> Last weekend, we drove up to Snow Valley to go skiing.
> I went with my friends to the movies Friday night.
> In April I have to return to work, but I will enjoy it.
> This weekend I am going to play in a racquetball tournament.
> My father asked me to pick up some nails for him at the hardware store.

AUDITORY PERCEPTION
How many syllables are in the word?

company (3)	anniversary (5)
candy (2)	encyclopedia (6)
potato (3)	school (1)

CLASSIFICATION
Which two go together?

> *sneeze* - pancake - moon - *cold* - king
> belt - *wand* - towel - glass - *magician*
> fall - pipe - *stereo* - pool - *CD*
> *pepper* - sun - tire - *salt* - spider
> judge - *brush* - spout - *paint* - silo
> leaves - camera - *mistakes* - *eraser* - shirt

40

SEMANTICS

Give two meanings for these words.

    toe, tow

    wood, would

    your, you're

    blew, blue

    lead, led

    ate, eight

SYNTAX/MORPHOLOGY

Change these sentences to the past tense.

    Adam *throws* a terrific fast ball.

    She *speaks* well in front of an audience.

    Leslie *makes* straight A's in chemistry.

    Tom *sells* posters at the swap meet.

    I *teach* aerobics during the summer.

    José *swims* to get in shape for baseball.

GENERAL QUESTIONS

What kind of animal is each of these characters?

    Moby Dick

    Old Yeller

    Charlotte from *Charlotte's Web*

    Bambi

    Black Beauty

    Dumbo

AUDITORY MEMORY

Repeat these sentences.

> Last weekend a friend of mine enlisted in the Marines.
>
> Would you mind closing the window? I'm freezing!
>
> Todd ran seven miles without stopping for a drink of water.
>
> My brother and I went to the beach Sunday to ride the waves.
>
> My parents are going to give me a car when I go to college.
>
> The boy was kidnapped and found wandering in a daze the next day.

AUDITORY PERCEPTION

Give two words that rhyme with:

aim	brush
bar	clean
blue	ever

CLASSIFICATION

Which one doesn't belong?

> Paris - Rome - *Chicago* - London
>
> cactus - sand - tortoise - *fish*
>
> classical - rock - jazz - *guitar*
>
> sparrow - crow - robin - *mouse*
>
> raft - *stick* - sailboat - steamship
>
> *pincushion* - thread - scissors - needle

SEMANTICS

Give a word that means the same as:

dwelling

ill

wet

insect

tiny

quick

SYNTAX/MORPHOLOGY

Combine these sentences into one sentence.

Jamie got on the bus. The bus was going to the beach.

Tom hit the ball. The ball broke the window.

Angie liked the dress. The dress was in the window.

The boy was lost. We found the boy.

Mom made the sandwiches. We ate the sandwiches.

Mack passed chemistry. Mack failed history.

GENERAL QUESTIONS

Name something that:

is fastened to the wall

you must look up to see

you see only in the summer

you see only in the winter

you can't see during the day

has wheels but can't roll

AUDITORY MEMORY

Repeat these sentences.

What are you planning to do over spring vacation?

At the end, the two girls began weeping very quietly.

Today in physical education, we played badminton.

This summer I plan to visit my uncle who lives in Denver.

Rick shook my hand so hard and so long that it hurt.

I can't wait until I am 18 because I will be able to vote.

AUDITORY PERCEPTION

Give me a word beginning with this sound.

/v/	/ɾ/
/h/	/s/
/f/	/b/

CLASSIFICATION

Complete these sentences.

Ring is to *jewelry* as *coat* is to (*clothing*).

Employer is to *employee* as *teacher* is to (*student*).

Week is to *month* as *month* is to (*year*).

Aviary is to *kennel* as *bird* is to (*dog*).

Racquet is to *bat* as *tennis* is to (*baseball*).

Sew is to *needle* as *cut* is to (*scissors*).

SEMANTICS

Why don't these sentences make sense?

> A new bridge was built connecting California and Hawaii.
>
> Take the rake to the garden and dig a hole for the plant.
>
> The clock on my wrist said it was 2:00.
>
> When I stepped on the scale last night, I weighed 109 feet.
>
> The pitcher threw the ball for a touchdown.
>
> When I walked outside, the sun was shining and the sky
> was blue, so I put up my umbrella.

SYNTAX/MORPHOLOGY

Change these questions to statements.

> Did John go water skiing?
>
> Does Mary like vegetables?
>
> Did Shawn go to the beach last summer?
>
> When is Mark going home?
>
> Will Carissa go with me?
>
> Would they like to go to Disneyland?

GENERAL QUESTIONS

Answer these questions.

> What is a fruit that begins with "o"?
>
> What is the third month of the year?
>
> How many times is the letter "t" in the word "potato"?
>
> What are the names of the days of the week?
>
> What are two vegetables that grow underground?
>
> When does winter begin?

AUDITORY MEMORY
Repeat these sentences.

> If you could have one wish come true, what would that wish be?
>
> On rainy days, I usually get a ride from Mom.
>
> I am planning on asking Amy to the dance.
>
> The old tree had to be chopped down because it was almost dead.
>
> The mouse scurried across the floor and began nibbling on the crumbs.
>
> After Larissa graduates from high school, she plans to attend junior college.

AUDITORY PERCEPTION
Give two words that rhyme with:

hair	sight
add	car
bank	fellow

CLASSIFICATION
Complete these sentences.

> *Third* is to *fourth* as *fifth* is to (*sixth*).
>
> *Pitcher* is to *baseball* as *quarterback* is to (*football*).
>
> *Pen* is to *write* as *ruler* is to (*measure*).
>
> *London* is to *Rome* as *England* is to (*Italy*).
>
> *Stoop* is to *stand* as *low* is to (*high*).
>
> *General* is to *specific* as *state* is to (*name of state*).

SEMANTICS

Which is more?

> hate - despise - dislike
>
> adore - care for - like
>
> genius - brilliant - smart
>
> red - maroon - scarlet
>
> promise - under oath - pledge
>
> exasperated - frustrated - frantic

SYNTAX/MORPHOLOGY

Correct these sentences.

> I ain't going to do it!
>
> I and Jim went to the mall.
>
> He adopted them attitudes.
>
> Which one of you stoled it?
>
> The family are leaving tomorrow.
>
> The swimmer swimmed four lengths of the pool.

GENERAL QUESTIONS

What reference book would you use to find these?

> the longest river in the world
>
> the meaning of the word *panacea*
>
> a magazine article on acid rain
>
> the types of crops grown in Bolivia
>
> three synonyms for cheerful
>
> the average rainfall in Germany

AUDITORY MEMORY
Repeat these sentences.

> During the past school year, I earned 85 credits.
>
> In two weeks, my sister is going to lend me her car.
>
> Last night at the store, I bought chips, dip, Coke, and three ice cream bars.
>
> A good friend of mine invited me over to his house to swim.
>
> The student has been suspended from school for fighting with some other kids.
>
> This year my New Year's resolution was to do two hours of homework a day.

AUDITORY PERCEPTION
Give two words that rhyme with:

shell	print
cow	just
clump	pool

CLASSIFICATION
Which one doesn't belong?

> clam - oyster - *seaweed* - scallop
>
> scamper - scurry - skip - *fast*
>
> globe - *pear* - ball - grapefruit
>
> newspaper - book - *picture* - letter
>
> grasshopper - *snail* - housefly - ladybug
>
> tape - glue - *scissors* - staple

SEMANTICS

Quickly name something real or imaginary that would make you feel:

horrified	apprehensive
affectionate	eager
conceited	exhausted

SYNTAX/MORPHOLOGY

Correct these sentences.

Salley is the beautifulest girl in school.

I won him, 21 to 15.

At the zoo, I saw ten mooses.

It took three firemens to put out the fire.

We went to the movies tomorrow.

Bob and Sue standed in line for two hours.

GENERAL QUESTIONS

Answer these questions.

How old must you be to vote in a national election?

What are four colors?

If Karen's baby was three days old on Independence Day, when is the baby's birthday?

What day is added to the calendar in leap year?

What sport can be played without a ball?

What are three ways you could get to school without driving a car?

Warm-Up #22

AUDITORY MEMORY
Repeat these sentences.

> We have scheduled your appointment for 11:30.
> I will be eligible for driver's training next fall.
> Every day Sue walks home from school with Charlene and Cathy.
> After the storm, huge logs and sections of branches were washed ashore.
> The only sound in the forest was the wind blowing through the branches.
> If you don't know the meaning of the word, look it up in the dictionary.

AUDITORY PERCEPTION
What is this word?

a-te   c-oa-s-t
b-ee-t   f-e-m-a-le
l-u-n-ch   i-n-tr-o-d-u-ce

CLASSIFICATION
Add an appropriate word.

table - sofa - desk (furniture)
daisy - rose - carnation (flower)
marble - tennis ball - golf ball (something round)
pillow - kitten - cloud (something soft)
turtle - oyster - armadillo (shell)
cola - coffee - tea (beverage)

SEMANTICS

Quickly name something real or imaginary that would make you feel:

worried   comfortable

nervous   bashful

puzzled   tired

SYNTAX/MORPHOLOGY

Correct these sentences.

Who is gooder, you or Michael?

Two oxes pulled the cart down the street.

They is a really nice family.

I am feeling sickness today.

Mr. Sanchez speaked very well of you.

A herd of sheeps grazed on the grass.

GENERAL QUESTIONS

What kind of tool would you use to:

cut the grass

lift a piano

make a hole in wood

remove weeds from a flower bed

drive a nail

clear a drain

Warm-Up #23

AUDITORY MEMORY
Repeat these sentences.

> The spaghetti that I had eaten yesterday made me ill.
>
> Bill picked up the orange that had fallen from the tree and ate it.
>
> Matt made the shirt that he wore to school on Friday.
>
> Turning the corner by the school, I saw the dog that was missing.
>
> Walking up to the teller, the bank robber pulled out a gun and demanded the money.
>
> A violent storm blew up, forcing the small craft toward the shore.

AUDITORY PERCEPTION
Give me a word ending with this sound.

/v/	/tʃ/
/f/	/z/
/p/	/s/

CLASSIFICATION
Complete these sentences.

> *Flock* is to *bird* as *herd* is to (*cattle*).
>
> *Crimson* is to *red* as *beige* is to (*brown*).
>
> *Curtain* is to *drape* as *rug* is to (*carpet*).
>
> *Quarter* is to *coin* as *dollar* is to (*bill*).
>
> *Touchdown* is to *home run* as *football* is to (*baseball*).
>
> *Ballet* is to *dance* as *rock* is to (*music*).

SEMANTICS
Give two meanings for these words.

hour, our

peace, piece

road, rode, rowed

sail, sale

steal, steel

waste, waist

SYNTAX/MORPHOLOGY
Is this a complete sentence?

The girl who bought my car.

Come over here!

After we finish our assignment.

Paul took Maureen to the dance.

My dad said that if I made all A's.

She gave the paper to Joyce.

GENERAL QUESTIONS
Answer these questions.

What are the names of three insects?

How much does it cost to mail a letter?

What are the names of three kinds of dogs?

Who are two famous actors?

What is an odometer?

If you needed to drive a nail and couldn't find a hammer,
   what could you use?

Warm-Up #24

AUDITORY MEMORY
Repeat these sentences.

> The students who belonged to the service club had a candy drive to raise money.
>
> Anyone who has completed driver's training is eligible to apply for a license.
>
> Of all my classes this summer, Spanish is the most difficult.
>
> The woman for whom we worked last weekend paid us by check.
>
> Toleka and Toby, my cousins from Ohio, had a great time learning to bodysurf.
>
> After we finished working on the paper drive, we all met for a pizza.

AUDITORY PERCEPTION
What is this word?

> / unk / ed (bunk bed)
> geogra / y (geography)
> air / ond / tion (air condition)
> / alen / ar (calendar)
> /ote / ook (notebook)
> / ome / ork (homework)

CLASSIFICATION
How are these two alike?

butterfly - wasp	glasses - crutch
octopus - spider	mittens - gloves
hourglass - watch	zoo - prison

SEMANTICS
Which is more?

sad - brokenhearted - sorrowful
ecstatic - elated - happy
scared - frightened - terrified
sleepy - tired - exhausted
humorous - hilarious - funny
like - love - infatuated

SYNTAX/MORPHOLOGY
Change these statements to questions that can be answered yes or no.

Our high school won the basketball championship.
The drill team will practice on Saturday.
Julie has to wash her hair tonight.
She left her jacket at the stadium.
I am going to pass algebra this semester.
Steve talked to Paul about the party.

GENERAL QUESTIONS
Answer these questions.

What are two sports that use a net?
How much money is a grand?
Who is a cartoon character from the funny papers?
If you wanted to find out the capital of Bolivia, where would you look?
What are two foods that are eaten raw?
How many days are in the month of April?

AUDITORY MEMORY
Repeat these sentences.

> After finishing his homework, Jim watched the tennis match on television.
>
> Although Katie had enough money to buy a car, she decided to wait.
>
> Even if you pass the test, you must do extra credit work to get an A.
>
> Because he had a report due in his English class, Myka decided not to go to the movie.
>
> Because she had to pay for her own car expenses, Rana got a job at the library.
>
> When Frank earns extra money, he puts it into his savings account.

AUDITORY PERCEPTION
What is this word?

pl-a-ce	tr-a-ff-i-c
r-oo-f	w-e-l-c-o-me
s-u-pp-er	v-a-c-a-tion

CLASSIFICATION
Add an appropriate word.

> tulip - rose - marigold - lily (flower)
> cider - coffee - tea - milk (beverage)
> curry - taco - ravioli - chow mein (foreign food)
> corduroy - silk - cotton - linen (fabric)
> bass - trout - perch - halibut (fish)
> almond - peanut - cashew - macadamia (nut)

SEMANTICS

Give a word that means the opposite.

    short

    old

    right

    decrease

    married

    artificial

SYNTAX/MORPHOLOGY

What is the contraction for:

    does not

    she had

    could not

    must not

    he will

    they had

GENERAL QUESTIONS

Answer these questions.

    What relationship are you to your uncle?

    What relationship is your sister to your mother and father?

    What relationship is your mother's sister to you?

    What relationship is your mother and father's son to you?

    What relationship is your uncle's daughter to you?

    What relationship is your brother's son to you?

Warm-Up #26

AUDITORY MEMORY
Repeat these sentences.

> Running for a class office was a great experience for Marcus.
> All of us who made an "A" on the test were given a free period.
> Eating candy bars in class is not allowed at our school.
> Of all the cookies I've eaten, Maria's are the best.
> Sitting on the beach all day, I got a terrible sunburn.
> Swinging his bat over his head, the batter stepped up to home plate.

AUDITORY PERCEPTION
How many syllables are in the word?

attendance (3)	mischievous (3)
masculine (3)	immediately (5)
mistakenly (4)	original (4)

CLASSIFICATION
In what category do these belong?

> bus - dune buggy - truck - jeep - car
> plum - lemon - apricot - orange - grape
> Munich - New Orleans - Moscow - Seattle - Salzburg
> ice skates - skis - toboggan - sled - snowshoes
> duckling - lamb - kid - cub - colt
> suitcase - purse - jar - bag - glass

SEMANTICS

Which is more?

> big - huge - large
>
> towering - high - tall
>
> tan - brown - beige
>
> fat - chubby - obese
>
> baby - toddler - child
>
> crazy - lunatic - mentally ill

SYNTAX/MORPHOLOGY

Correct these sentences.

> That is Tom shoe.
>
> I can run more fast than you.
>
> I am feeling very happiness today.
>
> Juanita is in ten grade.
>
> Mother holded the kitten for an hour.
>
> I set my pencil down over the table.

GENERAL QUESTIONS

What sport would you be playing if you received a penalty for:

> traveling (basketball)
>
> offsides (football)
>
> three-second violation (basketball)
>
> double fault (tennis)
>
> use of hands (soccer)
>
> high sticking (hockey)

AUDITORY MEMORY

Repeat these sentences.

The man who bought the car was my father's friend.

The program that I wanted to watch was on television last night.

The player who made the touchdown is in my social studies class.

We watched a movie about the monster who ate San Francisco.

The kids who went skiing had a great weekend.

The students who parked at the Community Center were given citations.

AUDITORY PERCEPTION

Give two words that rhyme with:

crab   sunk

snail   crook

thin   ham

CLASSIFICATION

Which two go together?

midnight - *morning* - Monday - *dusk*

violin - *guitar* - drums - flute

carrot - apple - *asparagus* - cheese

snake - dog - hawk - *lizard*

cat - *mouse* - *hamster* - cow

tomato - apple - *beet* - *potato*

SEMANTICS
Which is more?

furious - aggravated - mad

lovely - beautiful - gorgeous

peaceful - quiet - silent

cloudburst - sprinkle - rain

dark - pitch black - dusk

hot - warm - boiling

SYNTAX/MORPHOLOGY
Change these sentences from negative to positive.

Kristi and Leah won't make the team this year.

My dog doesn't chase cars.

Matt doesn't want to work at night.

She doesn't have enough money to pay for her own car insurance.

Our science teacher won't require a term paper.

Harrison didn't run for class treasurer.

GENERAL QUESTIONS
What do we call the young of these animals?

dog (puppy)

cat (kitten)

chicken (chick)

human (baby, child)

cow (calf)

whale (calf)

Warm-Up #28

AUDITORY MEMORY
Repeat these sentences.

> When I am 18, I plan to move out with a friend.
> Chris makes extra money on weekends by washing neighbors' cars.
> The janitors cleaned the school quickly so they could go home early.
> Do you think keeping animals caged up is humane?
> I wish I could transfer out of Ms. Green's class so I could play volleyball.
> If I am tardy one more time, I will have to serve one hour of detention.

AUDITORY PERCEPTION
What is this word?

air / ane (airplane)   me / al (metal)
/ ews / aper (newspaper)   sci / ors (scissors)
mo / ie (movie)   / ider / eb (spider web)

CLASSIFICATION
Which one doesn't belong?

car - *glider* - ski boat - train
spoon - knife - *bowl* - fork
bird - airplane - helicopter - jet
dictionary - *novel* - textbook - encyclopedia
rain - snow - *cloud* - hail
baseball - football - tennis - *swimming*

SEMANTICS

Which is more?

tiny - microscopic - small

breakable - fragile - delicate

damp - humid - drenched

dull - boring - monotonous

chilly - freezing - cold

soaked - wet - damp

SYNTAX/MORPHOLOGY

Is this a correct sentence?

I don't want the most smaller piece.

I want the biggest candy.

The room is more warmer inside.

She wore her ugliest shoes today.

The homecoming queen was the most beautifulest.

Your shirt is more wetter than the others.

GENERAL QUESTIONS

Answer these questions.

What is a mammal that lives in the water?

What is a state that begins with the letter "T"?

What is something that is rectangular?

What is another name for a drugstore?

Which is longer, a mile or a kilometer?

What is the product of two and three?

Warm-Up #29

AUDITORY MEMORY
Unscramble these sentences.

> tooth pulled my dentist the
> made my sister lunch my
> book you did that read
> dollars Mikaela me gave ten
> hair had yesterday my cut I
> breakfast had we eggs for

AUDITORY PERCEPTION
Give two words that rhyme with:

> oar
> eye
> rough
> wave
> catch
> table

CLASSIFICATION
Which two go together?

> *ring* - shirt - glasses - *necklace*
> nose - *moustache* - *beard* - pencil
> *gold* - *copper* - dime - drawer
> pink - crayon - *needle* - *pin*
> *heart* - arm - *liver* - shoe
> *second* - *minute* - noon - book

64

SEMANTICS

Give a word that means the same as:

delicious

rapid

odd

giggle

tidy

sleepy

SYNTAX/MORPHOLOGY

Combine these sentences into one sentence.

We saw the movie. The movie was interesting.

Kim found the wallet. The boy lost the wallet.

Hannah got a ticket. Hannah was speeding.

The car belongs to Steve. The car is in the garage.

We mowed the lawn. We watered the lawn.

Les hit a fly ball. Jeff caught the fly ball.

GENERAL QUESTIONS

What sport would you be playing if your position were:

tailback (football)

goalie (soccer, hockey)

forward (basketball, hockey)

wide receiver (football)

catcher (baseball)

AUDITORY MEMORY
Unscramble these sentences.

> at that look
> door answer the
> brown dog is the
> the today store closed is
> the fighting cats are dogs the
> the made wall is of brick

AUDITORY PERCEPTION
What is this word?

> p-ie
> ch-ee-se
> f-oo-t-b-a-ll
> t-y-pe
> m-a-n
> f-i-ve

CLASSIFICATION
Complete these sentences.

> *Man* is to *nephew* as *woman* is to (*niece*).
> *Good* is to *better* as *bad* is to (*worse*).
> *Goose* is to *geese* as *deer* is to (*deer*).
> *Old* is to *new* as *ancient* is to (*modern*).
> *Hand* is to *foot* as *wrist* is to (*ankle*).
> *Window* is to *dress* as *glass* is to (*fabric*).

SEMANTICS

Give a word that means the opposite.

work

neat

rare

import

dull

sturdy

SYNTAX/MORPHOLOGY

Change these words to mean more than one.

fish

police officer

tooth

air

wallpaper

mouse

GENERAL QUESTIONS

Answer these questions.

What do we call Egyptian writing?

What was the purpose of the pyramids?

What is a famous river in Egypt?

What is the Sphinx?

What were the ancient rulers of Egypt called?

Who was King Tut?

AUDITORY MEMORY
Unscramble these sentences.

> here over come
>
> are how you
>
> like I that sweater
>
> going when are you home
>
> is color what car your
>
> bike every day my school ride I to

AUDITORY PERCEPTION
What is this word?

> k-i-ck
>
> m-u-s-i-c
>
> s-o-cc-er
>
> t-ur-k-ey
>
> f-i-re
>
> p-u-n-t

CLASSIFICATION
How are these alike?

> boots - sandals
>
> hour - week
>
> paper clip - staple
>
> crayon - chalk
>
> marble - tennis ball
>
> carrot - turnip

SEMANTICS

Give a word that means the same as:

    defeat

    fast

    tardy

    correct

    overweight

    funny

SYNTAX/MORPHOLOGY

What is the contraction for:

    will not

    have not

    I will

    are not

    I am not

    it is

GENERAL QUESTIONS

What kind of animal group is a:

    swarm (bees)

    herd (cattle, etc.)

    school (fish)

    flock (birds, sheep)

    crowd (people)

    pride (lions)

AUDITORY MEMORY

Unscramble these sentences.

> happy you are
>
> dishes do the
>
> chocolate good milk is
>
> salty ocean is the very
>
> have you to store the been
>
> stack the high papers of was

AUDITORY PERCEPTION

What is this word?

> f-ea-th-er
>
> n-a-me
>
> b-ea-ch
>
> c-a-m-er-a
>
> b-a-th
>
> l-e-g

CLASSIFICATION

Complete these sentences.

> *Chemistry* is to *science* as *algebra* is to (*math*).
>
> *Arm* is to *body* as *bedroom* is to (*house*).
>
> *Latitude* is to *horizontal* as *longitude* is to (*vertical*).
>
> *Money* is to *bank* as *book* is to (*library*).
>
> *Finger* is to *nail* as *head* is to (*hair*).

SEMANTICS
Why don't these sentences make sense?

Yesterday, I saw a car speeding along the highway without an engine.

I was in such a hurry this morning that I had to wash my face and blow-dry my hair at the same time.

When your gas gauge reads empty, you need to fill up the car with oil.

Scuba diving in streams is a lot of fun.

Suzanne's dress was much too long, so her mother lengthened it.

Tuna salad is one of my favorite desserts.

SYNTAX/MORPHOLOGY
Combine these sentences into one sentence.

He washed the dishes. He dried the dishes.

Luke has algebra this semester. Luke has French this semester.

Mary is my friend. Mary bought a car.

Marty went to the game. Angie went to the game.

I like potatoes. I don't like spinach.

Matt came over. We did our homework.

GENERAL QUESTIONS
Answer these questions.

How often are the Olympics held?

What kind of event is the downhill?

What are two sports in the Winter Olympics?

Who has competed in the Olympics?

For which Olympics, Summer or Winter, would you expect to watch the luge event?

Where were the last Summer Olympic games held?

AUDITORY MEMORY

Unscramble these sentences.

paint the dried

wet was it

was class filled the

there move over the table

the fast flowers very grew

the ink out of ran pen teacher's

AUDITORY PERCEPTION

Give me a word ending with this sound.

/p/	/m/
/dʒ/	/ʃ/
/ŋ/	/k/

CLASSIFICATION

Add an appropriate word.

lamp - flashlight - candle - fire (gives light)

violin - guitar - kite - marionette (has strings)

radio - letter - television - telegram (way to communicate)

inch - meter - yard - mile (length)

scale - thermometer - ruler - tape measure (used for mea-
surement)

boulevard - street - avenue - place (name for thoroughfare)

SEMANTICS

Quickly name something real or imaginary that would make you feel:

interested	satisfied
excited	sick
lazy	bored

SYNTAX/MORPHOLOGY

Change these sentences from the positive to the negative.

Jacque finished his homework.

He fell off his skateboard.

Marissa sings in the church choir.

I took Spanish last semester.

We are going to the movies on Saturday.

Marianne wrote her term paper for social studies.

GENERAL QUESTIONS

Who invented each of the following?

cotton gin (Eli Whitney)

steam engine (Robert Fulton)

light bulb (Thomas Edison)

telegraph (Marchese Marconi)

telephone (Alexander Graham Bell)

dynamite (Alfred Nobel)

AUDITORY MEMORY
Unscramble these sentences.

> like I you
> home now come
> is it time what
> much will how it cost
> walking the boys school are to
> behind pool a has the house ours

AUDITORY PERCEPTION
What is this word?

> sh-oe
> s-i-s-t-er
> d-a-n-ce
> s-ur-f
> f-a-th-er
> p-ay

CLASSIFICATION
Add an appropriate word.

> crash - thump - bang (sound)
> camel - falcon - turtle (animal)
> penny - dime - quarter (change)
> sunny - windy - foggy (weather)
> copper - steel - gold (metal)
> beige - turquoise - lavender (color)

SEMANTICS

Give a word that means the same as:

dark

sick

said

peace

smile

dirty

SYNTAX/MORPHOLOGY

Correct these sentences.

We will ate lunch at school tomorrow.

We have mouses in our garage.

Ruth and John is going to the school dance.

Our school winned the basketball championship.

Leslie and me studied for our exam together.

Robert bought hisself a motorcycle.

GENERAL QUESTIONS

Answer these questions.

What is something that is purple?

How many weeks are in a month?

What are two things that are spherical?

What are three things you keep in a medicine cabinet?

Who is a President that was assassinated?

What is the capital of Mexico?

AUDITORY MEMORY

Unscramble these sentences.

down sit now

is name my Allen

close please the door

notebook my red is

potatoes pass the plate me of

to type do you how know

AUDITORY PERCEPTION

Give two words that rhyme with:

floor	how
ice	stop
rat	hurt

CLASSIFICATION

Which one doesn't belong?

English - math - science - *announcements*

lemon - sun - grapefruit - *tomato*

Honda - Toyota - *Chevrolet* - Porsche

news - *chair* - comedy - cartoon

May - September - *summer* - January

dictionary - encyclopedia - *novel* - atlas

SEMANTICS
Give two meanings for these words.

> fare, fair
>
> for, four, fore
>
> heel, heal, he'll
>
> knew, new, gnu
>
> knight, night
>
> no, know

SYNTAX/MORPHOLOGY
Combine these sentences using *because* or *so*.

> Emily didn't go in the water. The water was cold.
>
> Karla got her allowance. Karla went to the movies.
>
> She left her sweater in the car. It was warm outside.
>
> It was raining. We didn't go to the beach.
>
> Brad made himself a sandwich. He was hungry.
>
> Emery failed his English test. Emery didn't study.

GENERAL QUESTIONS
Answer these questions.

> What season comes after spring?
>
> How many times is the letter "s" in the word Mississippi?
>
> What is the name of an ocean?
>
> In what month do we celebrate Independence Day?
>
> How often do we elect a president?
>
> What are two spices?

AUDITORY MEMORY
Unscramble these sentences.

twenty laps swam Jim

sport my is baseball favorite

house over the flew jet the

cake Anne we a for birthday baked

the caught for he a pass touchdown

out the candle burned

AUDITORY PERCEPTION
What is this word?

/ eadache (headache)

/ ennis / oe (tennis shoe)

/ un / ine (sunshine)

/ alen / ine (valentine)

ele / tri / al (electrical)

mo / entary (momentary)

CLASSIFICATION
In what category do these belong?

jail - badge - uniform - tickets - court

watch - squint - wink - blink - stare

snow - sleet - hail - rain - drizzle

telescope - periscope - microscope - binoculars

brake fluid - water - oil - gasoline - antifreeze

crayon - pencil - chalk - pen - marker

SEMANTICS
Give a word that means the same as:

smart

strange

hot

breeze

angry

boy

SYNTAX/MORPHOLOGY
Change these statements to questions.

Brad likes watermelon.

May looks like her sister, Erin.

It is too difficult for you.

The movie starts at 7:00.

Peter is finished with his homework.

This is a daisy.

GENERAL QUESTIONS
Whose picture is on a:

$1 bill (Washington)

$5 bill (Lincoln)

$10 bill (Hamilton)

$20 bill (Jackson)

penny (Lincoln)

nickel (Jefferson)

AUDITORY MEMORY
Unscramble these sentences.

> home go let's
> am tired I
> going where you are
> house vacuum the please
> help thank for your you
> own I wish had I my car

AUDITORY PERCEPTION
Give two words that rhyme with:

> cat
> cab
> lace
> fad
> wade
> nag

CLASSIFICATION
Which two go together?

> yard - *walk* - school - *run*
> *pencil* - book - *pen* - paper
> *cup* - table - *fork* - floor
> math - numbers - *addition* - *subtraction*
> *truck* - walk - *motorcycle* - wind
> *Spain* - Frankfurt - *Sweden* - government

SEMANTICS

Give a word that means the same as:

small

happy

eat

war

road

fat

SYNTAX/MORPHOLOGY

Correct these sentences.

He quick parked the car.

Him got the ball on the 50-yard line.

I haven't aten yet.

I love them little puppies.

She growed tomatoes and beans in her garden.

She kept the biggest piece of cake for himself.

GENERAL QUESTIONS

In what country would you find these major cities?

Boston

Belfast

Zurich

Rome

Cancun

Sydney

AUDITORY MEMORY

Unscramble these sentences.

> leg Landon his broke
>
> did team the you make
>
> me school after meet
>
> friend her called Larissa
>
> my I dress tore
>
> trumpet Cassandra band the in plays

AUDITORY PERCEPTION

What is this word?

> h-o-t
>
> k-i-ng
>
> f-ie-l-d
>
> c-o-ll-ar
>
> a-sh-a-m-ed
>
> a-v-o-c-a-d-o

CLASSIFICATION

How are these two alike?

> van - bus
>
> spider - moth
>
> button - cuff
>
> snare drum - cymbals
>
> playing cards - clock
>
> committee - council

SEMANTICS

Why don't these sentences make sense?

Last night I fell asleep on the couch reading the television.

The house is nice except for the fact that the roof needs to be re-carpeted.

I have a new car that I bought two months from now.

I never take our pet parakeet outside because I'm afraid it might walk away.

Susan couldn't fall asleep last night so she turned off the lights and read a magazine.

Our dog said the litter of puppies she had was overdue.

SYNTAX/MORPHOLOGY

Change these words to mean more than one.

leaf   witch

sheep   water

ox   piece of chalk

GENERAL QUESTIONS

In what month do these holidays fall?

Christmas

Independence Day

Hanukkah

New Year's

Easter

Lincoln's Birthday

AUDITORY MEMORY

Unscramble these sentences.

> was for Jan class late
>
> a bought car I
>
> fall snow began to
>
> cookies Lee made
>
> rain it to started
>
> the fence jumped the horse

AUDITORY PERCEPTION

How many syllables are in the word?

> notebook (2)
>
> election (3)
>
> kayak (2)
>
> light (1)
>
> illuminate (4)
>
> microwave (3)

CLASSIFICATION

Which two go together?

> *hand* - *leg* - shoe - toothbrush
>
> *Jill* - Joseph - *Susan* - teacher
>
> addition - *52* - 10 - *59*
>
> *lemonade* - *coffee* - pork chop - fork
>
> *doll* - girl - *puzzle* - bedroom
>
> *baseball* - lawn - *hockey* - cart

SEMANTICS

Which is more?

> brand spanking new - fresh - recent
>
> worried - apprehensive - uneasy
>
> grotesque - displeasing - ugly
>
> thirsty - dehydrated - parched
>
> famished - hungry - starved
>
> gaunt - thin - emaciated

SYNTAX/MORPHOLOGY

Combine these sentences into one sentence.

> We are leaving at 9:00. Jesse is leaving at 10:00.
>
> This is a complete sentence. That one is not.
>
> You may see me now. You may see me later.
>
> Pam likes hamburgers. Brandi likes hamburgers.
>
> I am overweight. I plan to diet.
>
> Take out the trash. Water the lawn.

GENERAL QUESTIONS

Answer these questions.

> How many continents are in the world?
>
> What are the names of five countries?
>
> What is the largest country in the world?
>
> What is the smallest country in the world?
>
> What is a country in the Southern Hemisphere?
>
> What is a country in the Northern Hemisphere?

AUDITORY MEMORY
Repeat these sentences.

> The Ping-Pong ball typed the painting.
> The mushrooms started raining.
> The dishes cut my hair too green.
> Three cows flew out of the pizza.
> The spider borrowed the toast.
> Bob ate 15 clocks for lunch.

AUDITORY PERCEPTION
What is this word?

> i-n-c-h
> j-ea-n-s
> k-i-ss
> t-ea-ch-er-s
> h-a-pp-y
> c-o-mm-u-n-i-c-a-te

CLASSIFICATION
Which two go together?

> *hammer* - clock - *nail* - man
> shop - *letter* - *stamp* - ring
> *log* - dial - *fireplace* - butter
> *feather* - page - knife - hand - *bird*
> zipper - *sand* - *beach* - bottle - stem
> battery - *hour* - chime - *minute* - wing

SEMANTICS
Give two meanings for these words.

> sea, see, "c"
>
> tale, tail
>
> sun, son
>
> buy, bye, by
>
> coarse, course
>
> here, hear

SYNTAX/MORPHOLOGY
What is the contraction for:

> would not
>
> she is
>
> they will
>
> we had
>
> can not
>
> it will

GENERAL QUESTIONS
Answer these questions.

> What country is to the north of the United States?
>
> What are the names of two rivers?
>
> Where would you go to buy an oil filter?
>
> How many years of English are you required to take in school?
>
> Who is the President of the United States?
>
> Which comes first, dawn or dusk?

AUDITORY MEMORY

Repeat these sentences.

The last base Jon ate was a strike.

He coated the house with a new jacket.

I sang pancakes and sausages.

He laughed for extra shine on his French fries.

We tasted the parade at the corner.

She rang a convertible woman.

AUDITORY PERCEPTION

Give me a word ending with this sound.

/t/	/n/
/r/	/g/
/d/	/l/

CLASSIFICATION

Add an appropriate word.

sherbert - cake - ice cream (dessert)

can't - shouldn't - I'll (contraction)

fifth - second - third (ordinal number)

father - mother - aunt (relative)

January - May - September (month)

beef - pork - veal (meat)

SEMANTICS
Give a word that means the same as:

baby

hit

shut

cry

quick

ask

SYNTAX/MORPHOLOGY
Change these questions to statements.

Why don't they stay home?

Weren't you at the movies last night?

Could you come over right now?

Haven't you finished your homework?

Isn't it a beautiful day?

Are you leaving tomorrow?

GENERAL QUESTIONS
Answer these questions.

How many items are in a gross? (144)

What are two cars that are named for animals?

If you were measuring distance, would you use grams or
centimeters?

What are two sports that use a racquet?

What are three planets in the solar system?

What kind of tool would you use to remove a bicycle tire?

AUDITORY MEMORY
Repeat these sentences.

He ate his homework in the shower.

The book applauded loudly.

The tall fence sang briskly.

Nelson walks his piano every Thursday.

Corinne watched the invisible thunder.

The typewriter won the race in June.

AUDITORY PERCEPTION
What is this word?

/ oped (moped)

/ iver's / icense (driver's license)

/ ocial / udies (social studies)

foot / all (football)

/ emon (lemon)

/ ying / aucer (flying saucer)

CLASSIFICATION
Which two go together?

marigold - carpet - *rose* - elephant

couch - poster - *table* - door

watch - bracelet - *clock* - wall

garden - *rake* - *hoe* - brick

rain - *hail* - cloudy - cold

print - *front page* - book - *sports*

SEMANTICS
Give a word that means the opposite.

stay

whisper

expensive

float

export

correct

SYNTAX/MORPHOLOGY
Is this a complete sentence?

The paper floated.

I have seen it.

Close the door.

By my desk.

Write your name.

When the clock strikes twelve.

GENERAL QUESTIONS
Answer these questions.

What are two things that float?

What is the sum of four and two?

How many quarters are in two dollars?

Which is longer, an inch or a centimeter?

What are three things that are cold?

What do we call a group of cows?

AUDITORY MEMORY

Repeat these sentences.

> Bicycles bloom on Wednesday.
>
> Sweaters eat baked beans for breakfast.
>
> I wrote a long lettuce at the bakery.
>
> The birds sang the shovels loudly.
>
> The trumpet crawled across the ocean.
>
> The elephant rode the bicycle up the elevator.

AUDITORY PERCEPTION

Give me a word ending with this sound.

/θ/	/f/
/g/	/b/
/l/	/z/

CLASSIFICATION

Which two go together?

> king - *arrow* - carpet - *bow* - actor
>
> pan - *gloves* - vault - *boxing* - crown
>
> *pins* - card - book - stopwatch - *bowling*
>
> law - *paddle* - glue - *Ping-Pong* - coach
>
> *hoop* - carpet - glove - *basketball* - doctor
>
> hat - scissors - *whistle* - *referee* - dish

SEMANTICS
Give a word that means the same as:

flat

writer

wet

old

light

weak

SYNTAX/MORPHOLOGY
Change these sentences to the past tense.

I *am* late for my math class.

The referee *blows* the whistle to signal a penalty.

Rob *draws* very well.

She *drinks* a glass of orange juice with breakfast.

Lynn *drives* 55 mph to conserve gasoline.

Mika *sleeps* until noon on the weekends.

GENERAL QUESTIONS
On what continent would you find these countries?

Spain (Europe)

Canada (North America)

Brazil (South America)

China (Asia)

Egypt (Africa)

United States (North America)

93

AUDITORY MEMORY
Repeat these sentences.

> The hamburger tasted purple.
> All the cows sang sweetly.
> Good children seldom eat tables.
> They played very tall flowers.
> The eel came for lunch in March.
> The black flowers had orange feathers.

AUDITORY PERCEPTION
How many syllables are in the word?

> multiply (3)
> macaroni (4)
> operate (3)
> experience (4)
> communication (5)
> occupational (5)

CLASSIFICATION
In what category do these belong?

> black - red - green - yellow
> seal - walrus - dolphin - whale
> hat - glove - sweater - shirt
> arm - head - finger - leg
> station wagon - van - truck - jeep
> geography - English - social studies - health

SEMANTICS

Give a word that means the same as:

happy

pretty

quiet

sad

good

end

SYNTAX/MORPHOLOGY

Change these words to mean more than one.

woman

deer

goose

man

happiness

sister-in-law

GENERAL QUESTIONS

What sport would you be playing if you played for the:

Rams (football)

Celtics (basketball)

Brewers (baseball)

Toronto Maple Leafs (ice hockey)

Astros (baseball)

Lakers (basketball)

Warm-Up #45

AUDITORY MEMORY
Repeat these sentences.

> Pale spaghetti sparkled on the horizon.
> The giraffe went to the butcher shop for a haircut.
> The dentist broke the drum with ice skates.
> The piano played Monopoly on the ceiling.
> The short suit scrubbed the floor with toast.
> Checkers watch bananas on television.

AUDITORY PERCEPTION
What is this word?

> quar / er / ack (quarterback)
> home / oming (homecoming)
> / emporary (temporary)
> announ / ment (announcement)
> / ot / og (hot dog)
> / ollar / ill (dollar bill)

CLASSIFICATION
Which two go together?

> *harpoon* - net - *sword* - pencil
> motorcycle - *Ford* - *Plymouth* - skate
> Africa - *Illinois* - Italy - *Chicago*
> *waitress* - *lawyer* - uncle - cup
> belt - *boots* - *thongs* - car
> *living room* - house - *bedroom* - roof

SEMANTICS

Give a word that means the same as:

large

old

friend

day

red

clothing

SYNTAX/MORPHOLOGY

Change these sentences to the present tense.

Sharona *couldn't* keep up with the others.

The stamps *stuck* to the paper.

She *wrote* very well.

Marcie *spit* the watermelon seeds on the ground.

He never *wore* his ID bracelet in the pool.

Lettuce *grew* well in this area.

GENERAL QUESTIONS

Answer these questions.

What are two things made of metal?

Is there such a thing as a two-dollar bill?

What is the longest day of the year?

What is the name of a mountain range?

What tool would you use to clean a carpet?

What does the flag of Canada look like?

AUDITORY MEMORY

Repeat these sentences.

> The clock read square wagon wheels last night.
>
> Purple dogs cook flowered dishes.
>
> Music slept on the paper roof.
>
> Shooting rubber bands climbed out of the sky.
>
> Kristo baked the telephone in the sink.
>
> Well-behaved mice don't hammer cats.

AUDITORY PERCEPTION

Give me a word ending with this sound.

/k/	/b/
/ŋ/	/n/
/dʒ/	/t/

CLASSIFICATION

Complete these sentences.

> *Ten* is to *dime* as *hundred* is to (*dollar*).
>
> *Wet* is to *ocean* as *dry* is to (*desert*).
>
> *Meet* is to *met* as *shoot* is to (*shot*).
>
> *Bean* is to *vegetable* as *apple* is to (*fruit*).
>
> *Warm* is to *cool* as *hot* is to (*cold*).
>
> *Tiny* is to *large* as *weak* is to (*strong*).

SEMANTICS

Give two meanings for these words.

> right, write, rite
>
> hide
>
> high, hi
>
> to, two, too
>
> meat, meet
>
> nose, knows, no's

SYNTAX/MORPHOLOGY

Combine these sentences.

> Finish your homework. We can watch TV.
>
> Chico is going home. Mario is going home.
>
> Lionel is taking Zara to the dance. He likes her.
>
> Find an empty seat. Sit down.
>
> Plant the seeds. Soon they will sprout.
>
> Our team is the best. We will probably win the game.

GENERAL QUESTIONS

Answer these questions.

> What is something that is yellow?
>
> How many months are in a year?
>
> What are two things that have lids?
>
> What is the capital of the United States?
>
> What is something that gets smaller as you use it?
>
> What are two things that are square?

99

AUDITORY MEMORY
Repeat these sentences.

> Chubby burritos sang quietly to themselves.
> Cheering typewriters slept quietly on the desks.
> Driving tomatoes to school is dangerous.
> The sneaky mushroom devoured the babysitter.
> Her disagreeable glasses refused to stay awake.
> The toothbrush hid in the sour cream.

AUDITORY PERCEPTION
Give two words that rhyme with:

> chew
> hock
> west
> frown
> wing
> school

CLASSIFICATION
Which one doesn't belong?

> February - *Thursday* - March - August
> box - *plate* - sack - barrel
> tea - milk - *pie* - juice - coffee
> aunt - niece - *uncle* - sister - mother
> diamond - ruby - *gold* - opal - amethyst
> rake - *grass* - hoe - mower - shovel

SEMANTICS
Why don't these sentences make sense?

> Swimming right after a big meal is good for you.
>
> Only cross the street when the light is red.
>
> In springtime when the leaves begin to fall, I have a lot of yard work to do.
>
> The best kinds of exercise you can do are swimming, sitting, and jogging.
>
> At my high school, first period starts at 7:30 p.m.
>
> Every winter my father golfs in the Alps.

SYNTAX/MORPHOLOGY
Is this a complete sentence?

> The small brown cat.
>
> Taller than you.
>
> Are singing in the beautiful.
>
> Walk.
>
> Most parents like.
>
> The cat slept.

GENERAL QUESTIONS
Answer these questions.

> What kind of metal is used to make a penny?
>
> What is an 18-wheeler?
>
> How often do we have a leap year?
>
> If each half-hour of skating cost $1, how long could you skate for $3?
>
> What are two animals whose names begin with "B"?
>
> What is a ball used in an outdoor sport?

AUDITORY MEMORY
Repeat these sentences.

> The cat built bananas on the sidewalk.
> I poured shoes into her hand.
> Clocks become hungry for children.
> The angry truck was eaten by the 90-year-old woman.
> Eating painted Kleenex will make you fat.
> She flew under the laughing chair in the pond.

AUDITORY PERCEPTION
What is this word?

> / ocker / oom (locker room)
> / iving / oom (living room)
> / ic / onary (dictionary)
> ave / ue (avenue)
> / am / urger (hamburger)
> hall / ay (hallway)

CLASSIFICATION
How are these two alike?

> ocean - lake
> lead - steel
> desk - secretary
> mirror - pool
> wood - coal
> microscope - telescope

SEMANTICS

Quickly describe something real or imaginary that would make you feel:

depressed	lethargic
meek	cowardly
mellow	mysterious

SYNTAX/MORPHOLOGY

Change these sentences from positive to negative.

The girls made lunch for us.

We go to school in July.

Sonnie lost his health book.

Eli got a car for his birthday.

The boys ran 20 laps in gym.

Marita and Lucas will bake the cookies for the party.

GENERAL QUESTIONS

What sport would you be playing if you played for the championship in the:

Super Bowl (football)

World Series (baseball)

Davis Cup (tennis)

Stanley Cup (hockey)

Masters Tournament (golf)

World Cup (soccer)

AUDITORY MEMORY

Repeat these sentences.

> The flying pinball machine walked down the tree.
>
> The paper-mache mustache crawled across Grandma's face.
>
> Angry milk isn't of much use to purple cats.
>
> I rolled through the watery mashed potatoes and down the roast beef.
>
> The sparrow quickly tied a knot in the glass pencil.
>
> Bright telephones talked quietly in the dishwasher.

AUDITORY PERCEPTION

How many syllables are in the word?

destination (4)	strange (1)
strawberry (3)	association (5)
juggler (2)	evaporate (4)

CLASSIFICATION

Add an appropriate word.

> jacket - shoes - shirt (clothing)
>
> purple - orange - yellow (color)
>
> tiger - cheetah - leopard (type of cat)
>
> milk - tea - cola (beverage)
>
> baseball - softball - golf (sport played with a ball)
>
> apple - cherry - plum (fruit)

SEMANTICS
Give a word that means the same as:

all

asleep

before

best

boy

closed

SYNTAX/MORPHOLOGY
Combine these sentences into one sentence.

I like this dress. I don't like that one.

It is raining. I need to wear a raincoat.

The sweater and shirt look nice together. They are the
same color.

We are going skiing. There is a foot of new snow.

I am tired. I stayed up late.

Darcie doesn't want to go. I do.

GENERAL QUESTIONS
Answer these questions.

In what time zone do you live?

On what continent do you live?

What are four types of transportation you have used?

What is a country in Africa?

What is the name of a country that's an island?

What is the name of a group of islands?

AUDITORY MEMORY

Repeat these sentences.

> The brave little paper clip did somersaults across the dog's nose.
>
> As the clock struck 13, Cinderella turned into a dump truck.
>
> The doorknob stole three cookies out of the magazine.
>
> Watching yawning flies makes me depressed.
>
> I fell because I was talking to chalkboard dust.
>
> Tight rings make your eyes bulge out.

AUDITORY PERCEPTION

Give two words that rhyme with:

sew	butter
sound	boss
big	might

CLASSIFICATION

Complete these sentences.

> *Time* is to *place* as *when* is to (*where*).
>
> *Water* is to *liquid* as *rock* is to (*solid*).
>
> *Foot* is to *feet* as *deer* is to (*deer*).
>
> *Far* is to *near* as *least* is to (*most*).
>
> *Giggle* is to *laugh* as *cry* is to (*sob*).
>
> *Is* is to *was* as *are* is to (*were*).

SEMANTICS
Give a word that means the opposite.

different

empty

help

loose

hold

inhale

SYNTAX/MORPHOLOGY
Change these sentences from the present to the past tense.

I *drive* my car very carefully.

The clock is *striking* twelve.

I *am breaking* the pencil.

The wallpaper *is* blue and white.

I *am going* to the bank.

They *are writing* on the board.

GENERAL QUESTIONS
Answer these questions.

What are two things that have a switch?

How many days are in a week?

What is something that comes in liters?

What is something that is dry and can be poured?

What is the capital of (<u>your country</u>)?

What are two places that are quiet?